How to use this book

Follow the advice, in italics, given for you on each page.
Support the children as they read the text that is shaded in cream.
Praise *the children at every step!*

Detailed guidance is provided in the Read Write Inc. Phonics Handbook.

8 reading activities

Children:
* *Practise reading the speed sounds.*
* *Read the green, red and challenge words for the story.*
* *Listen as you read the introduction.*
* *Discuss the vocabulary check with you.*
* *Read the story.*
* *Re-read the story and discuss the 'questions to talk about'.*
* *Re-read the story with fluency and expression.*
* *Practise reading the speed words.*

Speed sounds

Consonants *Say the pure sounds (do not add 'uh').*

f ff	l (ll)	m	n	r	s ss	v ve	z zz s	(sh)	(th)	ng nk

b bb	c k (ck)	d	g (gg)	h	j	p	qu	t	w wh	x	y	ch tch

Vowels *Say the vowel sound and then the word, eg 'a', 'at'.*

at	hen	in	on	up	day	see	high	blow	zoo

*Each box contains one sound but sometimes more than one grapheme. Focus graphemes are **circled**.*

4

Green words

pi<u>ck</u>   e<u>gg</u>   just   fro<u>g</u>   ba<u>th</u>   spilt   <u>sh</u>e<u>ll</u>

splat   <u>th</u>is   tap   tri<u>ck</u>   mug

it   →   it's

Red words

<u>s</u><u>ai</u>d   to   was   cu<u>sh</u>ion*   <u>ch</u><u>air</u>*

* Red word for this book only

Vocabulary check

Discuss the meaning (as used in the story) after the children have read the word.

definition:

shell   *the hard outer coating of an egg*

Punctuation to note in this story:

Tom Mum	*Capital letters for names*
Tap A Pick	*Capital letters that start sentences*
.	*Full stop at the end of each sentence*
!	*Exclamation mark used to show surprise*
...	*Wait and see*

Tom's tricks

Introduction

Do you like playing tricks on people? Do you find it funny? In this story Tom has lots of fun playing tricks on his family. After a while Mum has had enough and sends Tom to bed, but when she goes to give Tom's sister a bath she thinks he's still playing tricks. Let's see what Tom gets up to.

Story written by Cynthia Rider
Illustrated by Tim Archbold

Tom put a trick egg in Mum's egg cup.
Tap ... tap ... splat!

"It's just a shell!" said Mum.

Tom put a trick frog
in Dad's mug.

Splash! Dad spilt
his drink.

Tom put a trick cushion on Gran's chair ...

and ...

Mum sent Tom to bed!

Mum went to bath Jen.
A big bug was in the bath.

"Tom, pick this trick bug up," said Mum.
Tom said, "But it's not a ..."

"Pick it up!"
said Mum.

And Tom did.

Help!

Questions to talk about

FIND IT QUESTIONS

✓ *Turn to the page*

✓ *Read the question to the children*

✓ *Find the answer*

Page 8: *How does Tom trick Mum?*

Page 9: *How does Tom trick Dad?*

Page 10: *How does Tom trick Gran?*
What does Mum think of Tom's trick? (pleased/cross/disappointed)
What does she do?

Page 12: *What does Mum think is in the bath?*
What does Tom try to tell her?

Page 13: *What do Mum and Jen think of the bug? (curious/scared/terrified)*